A Christian is not a passive onlooker who waits without acting. He is called to act and identify with those who suffer. Not just his own experience calls him to do so, but also the experience of his brother for whom Christ has suffered. 　　　　　　　　　　*Dietrich Bonhoeffer*

I LOVE A YOUNG MAN

by

Walter Trobisch

A private correspondence

United Society for Christian Literature
Lutterworth Press
London

2416
T77?
C ?

Copyright © Walter Trobisch 1964
Translated from the German "Ich liebe einen jungen Mann . . ."
French edition, « J'aime un jeune homme . . .» obtainable from
Editions Trobisch, Baden-Baden, Lange Strasse 50 (Germany)

Gesamtherstellung:
St.-Johannis-Druckerei C. Schweickhardt, Lahr-Dinglingen
(Germany) · 8942/1964

Preface

This booklet continues the private correspondence which was published under the title: I Loved A Girl . . .

While I was writing I kept thinking about the problems and troubles of those who have written to me in answer to the first volume. Thus readers from many African countries have indirectly become co-authors of this second book. My warm thanks to them for their confidence and for the service rendered to me and to future readers.

Because more people are involved this time, I have chosen only the most essential passages from the letters, and sometimes even summarized several letters into one. Greetings have been left out in order to avoid repetition. Now and then I have taken the liberty of putting into the form of a letter what in reality took place as conversation.

The answers, it is true, are not simple. I have deliberately not painted a black and white picture; I have deliberately recorded opinions with which I do not personally agree. All of us need training in seeing both sides. We must be ready to think, and think hard. No one can make a decision for someone else. The door remains open, and everyone must decide for himself. Before God.

Walter Trobisch
68 Mannheim
Traitteurstrasse 60
Germany

Note: Readers may not find the correspondence quite so easy to follow in this book, for now a larger number of writers make their contributions. They include:

François and Cecile
Pastor Walter Trobisch and his wife Ingrid
Pastor Amos and Monsieur Henri.

Dear Pastor T.

I am writing to you because I'm very upset. I haven't heard anything from François for almost four weeks.

He has spoken and written a great deal about you. That's why I dare to turn to you now.

You already know about how we got to know each other. It was in the bus. My aunt was in hospital and I was taking her child back to our village. The bus driver was in a hurry and started up again before I could get my luggage off the bus. François brought it back to me, and then stayed overnight at our home.

The next day he continued his trip, and went on to his mother's village. As you know, he had lost his job as a teacher because of getting into trouble with a girl.

Ever since I've been going to school in Y. we have written to each other almost every day. But since the beginning of June, he has not answered my letters.

I am very worried. What shall I do? Can you help me?

Cecile

Dear Cecile,

I am glad that you wrote to me. I feel as if we know each other, even though we've never met. Sometimes I even feel as if I know you better than people I meet every day. François has described you so vividly to me through his letters and conversations.

You know how close he has been to my heart ever since he was a school-boy. That unites us. Even more, it makes us allies. For we are in a battle . . .

You mention the trouble with that girl. He was really desperate when he lost his job. Fortunately he wrote to me right away. We corresponded then in great detail; you know about this, at least in part.

Above all he was disappointed with his church, which forbids him to take communion. He felt that he had been left in the lurch. He was so bitter, I was afraid he might lose his faith in God.

It is a miracle that the opposite happened: his faith became deeper. He let himself be forgiven. What God did for him was far greater than what men did. He had the courage to become very small before God. That is why God became very great to him. He threw himself into God's arms again.

That was a great moment. You must be thankful that you will receive a husband who has made such a decision.

He met you on his way home after that meeting with God. Was this just luck? Or a coincidence? It was more to François than that. It was a sign that God had not left him, that God still loved him in spite of everything. It strengthened his faith. Because of you, it was easier for him to trust God.

So it struck him all the harder then when your father asked for £150 as a bride price. His faith wavered. He wrote me an angry letter. It is a typical François letter. You know him already. As soon as an obstacle arises, he's ready to throw up everything: faith, love, God, state, church, me, and even you.

Here are a few samples from his letter:

"It is better to die than to live without life."

"I denounce those who are in responsible positions in our country, who eat up the money of the poor instead of breaking the monopoly of women held by the rich . . ."

"I denounce this totalitarian society, this dictatorship of the clan which demands that a girl marry the man her parents chose for her in order to maintain the financial balance of the family budget . . ."

"I denounce a custom which permits fathers to exploit their children more than any other nation has ever exploited us . . . a tradition which favours the exploitation of the couple by the clan . . ."

"I denounce the fathers who use their daughters to pay their debts, because they are too lazy to work."

"I denounce the Church . . . which punishes instead of helping . . ."

"Why does God show me His way without enabling me to walk in it? If the marriage of love remains the privilege of the rich, why doesn't God send the £150 which I need from heaven?"

This letter was written on June 3. Since then I haven't heard from François. Cecile, I've read this letter often. Each time I feel afresh that it is a great letter. He is so honest in his anger. He denounces everyone and everything except himself. He acts as if he were the first and only one to be asked to pay a bride price. But that's the way he is — our François. As long as something bothers others, he doesn't let it get under his own skin. But when it bothers him, he falls apart completely.

This letter should not remain unanswered. He simply expressed what many feel. At first this letter left me speechless. I didn't want to give him an easy answer which in the long run wouldn't help. Besides, I know all too well that we Europeans are to blame, at least in part, because a useful custom has been abused.

I was just thinking how I might answer in a helpful and effective way, when your letter arrived.

Cecile, I should like to ask you a favour. Will you answer this letter of François. You can help him here more than I can.

Let us be allies in the battle for your marriage. You show him that love is no forbidden land for Africans, as so many people think. You show him that Africans can and may love too.

This is not a question of money, but a question of faith. You show him that love does not accuse and denounce, but it fights.

There is still a paragraph in that letter which I haven't quoted yet. It says: "I denounce the girls who remain indifferent and passive in the face of such a curse as the dowry system; who let their parents have their way and who afterwards complain of their marriage which imprisons them more than walls or barbed wire."

Only you can answer this reproach. You show François that there are girls in Africa who are different.

I have great confidence in you, and I count on you.

Walter T.

Y. . . . ., July 20

Dear Pastor T.

Yesterday I did what you asked, and answered François' letter. I had to fight with myself for a long time. At first I didn't want to do it at all. Now at least I have tried. Enclosed you will see the result.

It was a difficult letter. I am still afraid to send it.

All last night I thought about what I should do. Then I thought of sending it first to you for you to look over. Please read it to your wife as well. If your wife also thinks that it is good to send it, then I will.

It's so hard to be completely honest and still not to wound. I am fearful about the answer. Perhaps I should omit the last four words. They are too strong.

Cecile

11

Dear François,

I love a young man. His name is François. Please don't doubt that for a minute when you read this letter.

I was attracted by you from the moment we first met in the autobus, and when you helped me to carry home my luggage. I felt even more drawn to you when you made no attempt that night to come to me. I felt then that you were not just interested in my body, but in myself. Not just in an hour of passion, but in a life-time together.

Just because I love you I dare to write you this frank letter.

Pastor Walter has quoted to me certain parts of the letter which you wrote to him on June 3. He has asked me to write and tell you what I think about it.

When I first read the letter, I was a little embarrassed — for you. But now I can at least understand why I have heard nothing from you for so long.

François, I understand you very well. I have kept all your letters. When I read them over and over again, I can begin to measure how my father's demand hit you. I know that you are poor. I know that you have lost your job. I can feel how much you love me . . .

Perhaps you are right, that the church has failed. Certainly you are right when you say that there is a lot of injustice in our young country. When the new and old bump against each other so suddenly, it can hardly be otherwise. You must never forget that revolutionary changes which took centuries to happen in Europe take place in our country in one generation. That is why a useful custom is abused, as Pastor Walter expressed it. But it is not only the Europeans who are guilty; we also are guilty.

There is a good thing too about the bride price. It shows us girls what we are worth to a man. That's just the way we are. We love the one who has to pay something for us, who has to fight for us, who has to conquer us.

At the beginning of this letter I wrote: "I love a young man." A man does not only denounce and accuse. A man fights. Denouncing God and the whole world doesn't change anything. I respect you only if you fight. And I can love you only if I respect you. That's why I bid you: fight for me. Fight with me for our marriage.

I don't want to leave you alone. I want to fight with you. You are right: most girls let themselves be sold as goods without showing a will of their own. I do not defend them. But your Cecile wants to be different.

The more we have fought together, the more precious our marriage will be. What just falls into our lap is not worth much. It doesn't bind us together.

I know that God means us to be together. Just how I know it, I can't explain. I just know it. Neither can I tell you now how we will find the money, or how my father will change his mind, or how you will find another job. And yet I know, deep down in my heart, that there is a way, so that some day we shall belong to one another.

God doesn't help us by letting money fall into our laps from heaven. But He goes with us step by step through all the difficulties, if we just hold His hand. What we need is not money, but faith, trust in God.

Once more: I love you. But I love the young man François, not the dish-cloth François.

Your Cecile

B. . . . ., July 22

Dear Cecile,

My husband read me your letter to François, as you asked him to do. You've hit the nail on the head — with the sure aim of true love.

But first I must say that I never dreamt that a girl of your age could write such a letter. I am all the more thankful because of it. I hope that we can get to know each other soon.

Yes, I know how hard it is to help without hurting. A doctor cannot always heal with a soothing ointment. Often he must use a knife to cut away the disease. In marriage each partner must be the doctor of the other one.

Only the one who is able to heal is also allowed to hurt. This is why love alone can dare to hurt with a good conscience. But love can do it and should do it. For real love is nothing sentimental and weak, but something firm and bold.

I was impressed above all that you have found the connection between respect and love.

In his explanation of the commandment, "You shall not

commit adultery", Martin Luther wrote as follows: "What does this mean for us? We are to fear and love God so that in matters of sex our words and conduct are pure and honourable, and husband and wife love and respect each other."

There is a close connection between the two — respect and love. Nevertheless to "respect" may have a much deeper meaning than you think. To respect means to appreciate, to find something worthy of love where no one else can discover it. I believe that a truly loving woman loves her husband even in his weakest hour, in his failure and defeat, even when he lets the leaves hang like a dried-up banana tree. Only the one who respects her partner in this way really loves him.

Go ahead and send your letter. It is a good letter. God blesses courage and honesty. Don't be afraid. If François' heart becomes black with anger, my husband will know how to clean it up again. Remember here too: "there is no fear in love."

Ingrid T.

E. . . . ., July 27

Sir,

. . . So you have succeeded in getting me to write to you again . . .

I have just received the letter from Cecile sent on by you. It was very clever of you to use her. You know me well and know exactly where I am most easily hurt . . .

But the letter had just the opposite effect from the one it should have had. She doesn't only criticize me, she even insults me.

And I thought she was an angel! Now the angel has shown her teeth . . .

But it's all right. At least I know now where I am. That's why I'm happy that she wrote me this letter. I have no more illusions. The disappointment makes it easier for me to bear my fate.

I possessed the first girl because she said I was no man. This one I will leave because she says I am no man. You wrote me once: "True courage here means to flee." So . . .!

What does it say in the Bible? Ephesians 5 : 22—24. I'll write it out for you, Mr. Pastor, so that you don't need to look it up:

Verse 22: "Wives, be subject to your husbands, as to the Lord."

Verse 23: "For the husband is the head of the wife, as Christ is the head of the church, his body, and is himself its Saviour."

Verse 24: "As the church is subject to Christ, so let wives be subject in everything to their husbands."

IN EVERYTHING! If she contradicts me now, what would it be like when we are married? Like all African men, I want a wife who obeys me — unconditional obedience in EVERYTHING. That's what the Bible says. Just as the Church is subject to Christ, so should wives obey their husbands. That is clear and without question.

I have been warned. Therefore I thank you.

F.

Dear François,   B. . . . ., August 3

This is just the way I thought you would react.

You are very foolish, François. Let me repeat it: very foolish.

I read Cecile's letter before she sent it to you. At her request I even read it to my wife. Both of us wish that many fathers and mothers, young men and girls, would read it, not only in Africa but also in Europe. It is a very unusual letter. We were moved by it.

Listen to me. Your Cecile is no piece of wood, no baby, no work-animal without a will of her own, no servant maid, but a very mature girl. I congratulate you on finding such a girl. You have no idea what a great gift it is that such a one loves you.

You wrote to me out of an angry heart after you had read the letter only once. You should never do that. Rather sleep on it for a night, so as to give yourself time to think. Read it again very slowly and quietly. Don't you understand how hard it was for Cecile to write it? That she said these hard things only because she loves you?

Don't you know? Love is not blind: love sees. It sees clearly the weak points and the faults of the other one; but it loves him nevertheless, including his weaknesses and faults.

You asked me once how someone could know whether he is truly in love. I answered you: by the fact that he is not put off by the faults of the other one. Of course, he does not love his faults, but loves the other one with his faults. He feels responsible for him.

Now it happens that Cecile loves you in this way. But instead of being thankful you are angry. Or did you think that you had no faults? Perhaps it would be impossible to love a person who had no faults.

Be honest. Everything that Cecile said is true. Your trouble is that you give up too quickly.

Yes, I know that criticism hurts. Especially criticism that is true. We are all very sensitive about this. A man is especially sensitive if he is criticized by a woman. It's true in our country too. But I think African men are oversensitive on this point. That's because the woman is never looked upon as an equal. One does not accept criticism from inferiors. This is the reason why so many marriages are empty and monotonous.

Before he was married one of my friends wrote his fiancée about what he expected from his future wife. I'll pick out only a few sentences of the long list he sent her. The first sentence was this:

"She must challenge me to the highest through absolutely honest criticism of me." Then it continued: "When she is disappointed in me, she must never withdraw her confidence." "Untiringly she must help me to overcome my weak sides." "She must never pretend, but must tell me honestly when I have hurt her." Do you understand? What he wanted was not a servant girl, but an equal partner who stood by his side before God. Only with such a partner can one become "one flesh" in the real depths of its meaning — a new, living being. Partnership includes the right to criticize.

And now Ephesians 5! If we pick out certain verses in

the Bible to prove that we are right, then we'd better be careful! Bible verses are no official stamp that can certify to the world: "Just look, even God agrees with me!"

God's word is like a hammer that breaks rocks in pieces; or like a sword that cuts into us, that hurts us, forms us, changes us. God's word challenges us to the highest.

You quoted verses 22—24 because they just suited you. Many thanks for copying them. But I opened my Bible nevertheless and read also verses 21 and 25.

Verse 21 emphasizes that submission is mutual, and it says: "Be subject to one another out of reverence for Christ."

Then come the verses you quoted, which explain what that means on the part of the wife. Verse 25 however shows what it means for the man. You left out this verse. It says: "Husbands, love your wives, as Christ loved the church and gave himself up for her."

That is a tremendous sentence. A whole life-time is not enough to understand its deep meaning.

How did Christ love His Church? He served it. He worked for it and helped it. He healed it, comforted it, and cleansed it. The Church was everything to Christ, and He gave everything for it, including His life.

Don't you see how God's word becomes a sharp sword that cuts and hurts us? Christ was not what we men like to be — a big chief or a sheik — who wants to be served. He was the slave of His Church. I use this word, because it hurts your African ears. Only as the slave of His Church was He its head. So also you are only the head of your wife in the measure in which you are her slave.

Even at that time the Church was not obedient to Him. It left Him in the lurch, and still does up to the present day. You have much to criticize in the Church. So have I. There is so much which is not beautiful in it, if you think about all the tensions and quarrels that go on. But this is the Church He loved. He died for it. Through His love He made it worthy of love.

If the Church obeys Him, then it does so, not because it has to, but because it wants to; for without Him the Church cannot live, just as a body cannot live without a head.

Don't you understand that Cecile really wants only one thing: to belong to you just as a body belongs to its head? Through her criticism she wants to attain only one thing: that you will be a head whom she gladly obeys.

That is why she is asking you to fight for her, just as Christ fought for His Church. Your fight for her is your service to her.

True courage here is not to run away, but to become mature.

As soon as possible you should go to Y. and talk to Cecile.

T.

E. . . . ., August 14

Dear Sir,

Again, what a letter! If I didn't know you so well, I should have torn it up. What can I say about it? What a nice sermon!

It's too bad you always look at things with one foot in heaven and the other one off the ground. You don't help me towards any practical solution.

The only practical suggestion which you have is in the last lines. But even that can't be carried out. How do you think that I could meet Cecile? If I picked her up after school, the news would be all over town right away, and there would be nasty gossip. She lives with her uncle. I wouldn't even dare to show myself there. A park with benches doesn't exist in the whole city. And I haven't a car. If I owned one I would also have money and I could get married.

You don't say a word about money. You talk only about love. But money and love are inseparable in Cameroun. Only those who have money can get married.

That is why I need money. I can only get it when I am working. I was a teacher at one of our church schools. The Church dismissed me.

Besides — if Christ is the head of the Church, and the Church is His body, both are one — how then is it possible that Christ forgives me and the Church does not?

Then too — I'm entirely on my own. Other young men have a father or family to support them. Here is my situation.

My grandfather had three sons: Tonye, Moise, and Otto. Tonye was the eldest. He wasn't a Christian because he had two wives. Moise, the middle son, was a catechist and had only one wife. She bore him four children, two of whom were sons. Otto, the youngest, had only one wife, Martha, who bore him one son, Jacques.

Otto died and Martha became a widow. That is a terrible fate in Africa. It goes together with the bride-price, which Cecile says gives her "value". She has no idea . . .

When a wife dies, it isn't so bad for a husband. He has lost his property. Property can be replaced if necessary. But a widow is like property that has lost its owner. She is helpless.

Martha was now a widow with her child Jacques.

Normally Moise as the next brother in line to Otto would have to marry Martha. But that wasn't possible. He was a Christian, and a catechist. He could have only one wife. That is the law of the Church. It is hard. The law of our customs and traditions would be more merciful. Because Moise was a catechist, he didn't dare to be merciful.

Moise did take the ten-year-old Jacques into his home and let him go to school. That was all that he could do.

So Martha was pushed on to Tonye. She became his third wife. He hated her from the beginning, and with her he hated Christianity. He neglected her, mistreated her and tormented her. She received neither clothes nor shoes; no hut in which to cook, not even a piece of soap. Nevertheless he had one child by her.

I was that child.

Tonye already had a son by his second wife, who was his favourite wife. He never recognized me as his son.

Only my mother cared for me. I was a dirty, neglected child. I had a skin disease because she had no soap to keep me clean. She could barely clothe me, and I was ashamed to go to school. I ran away and wandered around until I came to the Mission station. From there on you know my story.

Do you understand now why I can expect no help from my family? As far as my father goes, I do not exist, especially now I have become a Christian. My uncle Moise took my half-brother Jacques, and has four children of his own as well. I have only my mother. She has all she can do to live from her garden.

I cannot hope to inherit anything. Even if my father's favourite son died, both Jacques and Moise's two sons would come before me.

And now you say, I should go to Cecile. With empty hands? No.

F.

Dear François,

B. . . . ., August 20

Thank you for writing your whole story to me. We have known each other for almost ten years. That is how long it took us to get this far. Why?

Your letter showed me what poor ambassadors for our God we missionaries really are. When you came to me ten years ago you told me that your father was not concerned about either you or your mother. That was true. But I had no idea how much suffering and pain stood behind it. I took you in at our station and didn't ask any more questions.

23

We always make this mistake. We don't ask any more questions. We don't want to know too much. We are afraid that the burden might crush us. We fear the responsibility.

We missionaries think always we have done enough if we travel to Africa. It's true that we see you daily at the services and in school; but a great distance remains between us.

We're too lazy really to put ourselves in your shoes, to look at things with your eyes. Instead of this we shut our eyes and simply proclaim the Gospel as a law.

It's like someone discharging a pistol and shutting his eyes while he's doing it. He doesn't know whom he hits. Perhaps he hits a mother with her child. He really doesn't want to know.

How ashamed Christ must be of His missionaries! As I read your letter, I was ashamed before Christ and within myself. We are so unkind — so lazy in our thinking. Someone who has only one wife becomes a catechist. His brother who has two wives is excluded from the church. But in your story he actually plays the rôle of the Good Samaritan.

There just is no solution which applies to everybody. We cannot say: this is right for everyone, and that is wrong for everyone. Love is not lazy. We must take the trouble — the hard labour of love — to search out God's will afresh in each case.

Please forgive me for wanting to keep clear of this piece of work, and for not asking you any more questions.

Nevertheless, two things become very clear to me

through your letter. One is this: polygamy is not the solution. You know that better than I do, because you've experienced it yourself.

You asked me once if it was possible for a man to love several wives at the same time. You see now that it just doesn't work. Either there is no personal relationship between the man and his wives, or he has a favourite wife. In any case there is always want and emptiness, jealousy and hatred. Even the Bible testifies to that clearly when it describes polygamous relationships.

Just imagine now that your father's favourite son should die. What a fight would take place over the inheritance! Who would be able to unravel the tangle of the rights of the various parties? What a fight there would be, certainly with magic means too, between the brothers, half brothers, step brothers and cousins! We would certainly never wish to see it.

The other thing which is clear to me through your letter is this: that God has realized His plan in your life, in spite of all the mix-up of your family, in spite of the guilt of the Mission. In spite of everything He has called you to His kingdom.

God was in everything. In the suffering of your mother, in the lack of love of your father, God was there.

He brought us together. He saved you. He has taken you by the hand and has led you, in spite of your disobedience, in spite of my mistakes — led you to Cecile. What a work of God! *He* was not lazy. Even if we have all failed, He has not failed.

You said my letter was not practical enough. I can't show you any more than God has shown me for you. Often God does not show us the final solution. He only shows us steps to take.

In Psalm 119 it says: "Thy word is a lamp unto my feet, a light unto my path." God does not promise us headlights that will show us the whole way. He promises only a lamp, and that for our feet. A lamp does not light the path far ahead, but only a little way.

Your first step is to find work again. I am glad you thought of that yourself. I suggest you visit Pastor Amos, and ask him to re-employ you. I will write to him too and ask him if he will talk to Cecile's father himself. Is that practical enough for you?

And once more: there is no doubt about it, you must talk to Cecile. Don't worry about how you can meet her. A woman thinks with her heart, not with her head. Also in practical things she often has an idea before a man does. Have confidence in Cecile. Love has imagination.

T.

B. . . . ., August 20

Dear Cecile,

François has written to me again. At last he has come out of his hiding place. Your fine letter succeeded in bringing him out.

Now you must be ready. It is possible that he will be

waiting for you after school, when it starts again. It will be good for you to plan now where you can go, so that you can talk together in peace . . .

T.

B. . . . ., August 29

Dear Pastor Amos,

I am writing to you today concerning François. You know his story. I baptized him. You confirmed him. Then he became a teacher and I believe he did good work for three years.

Then he had a palaver with a girl. The case was made known among the pupils and he was denounced. Personally I have the impression that it was a planned trap. He was dismissed because of it, and was forbidden to attend the Lord's Supper for six months.

Then I had a detailed correspondence with him[1]. I'm enclosing copies of some of the letters, so that you have some idea about the case. Finally it led to a serious conversation in which I was able to help and advise him, and to a confession which went very deep. I cannot tell you more, because the secrets of confession are absolute. I can only testify as his counsellor that he was serious about his repentance, that he accepted the forgiveness of Christ, and that he dared to make a new beginning.

[1] W. Trobisch, I LOVED A GIRL . . . U. S. C. L.

We must stand by his side in this new beginning. You know that there are great temptations to faith after such a complete change round, especially when it is genuine. The devil seems to attack specially hard those who have made a decision deep in their hearts. That is why we must both show brotherly love to François in his first steps in the new life.

First I'd like to ask you to allow him to take the Lord's Supper. As far as I can see, the sacrament is only forbidden in the New Testament to those who persist in open sin in spite of many warnings. I cannot find a single case where one who has been repentant and who has confessed his sins has been placed under church discipline.

On the contrary, as his counsellor, I would encourage François to take communion on the next occasion. After his defeat, he will perhaps understand it now for the first time, and he will experience it for what it should be: the fellowship of Jesus with sinners.

When we exclude repentant sinners from the Lord's Supper, then it becomes exactly the opposite: a procession of righteous people who proclaim through their taking part that they either have not sinned, or have not been caught at it.

When the prodigal son found his way home again after his life in adultery, his father didn't let him wait for six months in a back room to see whether or not his repentance was genuine. No! He embraced him, accepted him immediately as his son, and ate with him as a sign of forgiveness!

That's exactly what made the Jews so angry at that

time. Jesus ate with sinners. That was blasphemy to them. That is why they crucifed Him. I ask myself, don't we get angry too? Aren't we crucifying Jesus afresh when we forbid sinners to have table fellowship with Him?

This is now a real problem for François. He writes to me: Christ has forgiven me, but not the Church. Are these two different things, Jesus Christ and the Church?

So, do you not think it possible that François might be re-employed as a teacher? That would be a visible sign that not the law but the Gospel rules in the Church; not punishment but forgiveness. I have a reason for asking this. François has got to know a girl. I think that they really love each other and are meant for each other. But now the question of the bride-price has come up. This question is a very difficult one for François, for he has no family to support him. You know the situation. The father of the girl is demanding £150 immediately. According to François, this is just a first instalment.

Could you not visit this family once? As an African, you would certainly get further than I could, and you could judge everything much better.

In any case, please give me your opinion and your counsel.

Walter T.

Dear Pastor Walter,

We've seen each other.

It was like that first meeting with Cecile. Everything is changed again.

For weeks now I have lived with my mother in a distant little village. For hours I've sat every day in a dimly-lighted hut. My thoughts kept going round in circles — always around the walls. I would stare at the pictures cut out of magazines which I had pasted on the wall, as if they could talk to me, give me advice. But always they were silent. At last I couldn't bear to look at them any more. I was trapped in my own prison.

And now the walls have been broken apart. There is freedom everywhere, even though outwardly nothing at all has changed. I'm just as poor as I was before. Only one thing has happened; we have seen each other again.

A friend took me with him in his car. He had to be back the same evening. So I had only two or three hours.

I waited at the entrance of the school. Pupils, both boys and girls, streamed out. Cecile was not among them. Those were terrible minutes.

Finally she came, the very last one. She must have seen me and waited until all the others were gone. She didn't look at me; she just held out her hand. With outstretched arm, I touched her finger-tips as indifferently as possible, as if we greeted each other in that way every day.

Then she said, as if she had been waiting for me: "There

are only two possibilities. We can go in the 'Red Donkey', or into the Catholic Church. It's always open."

I chose the Catholic Church, because I had no money for a restaurant. We had to walk for half an hour to get there. I went ahead, and she followed me a little distance behind. No-one would have guessed that we belonged together.

I would never have thought of going with her to the Catholic Church. It was really open. I asked myself, why are the Protestant Churches always closed?

We entered and sat down on a bench in one of the back rows. We didn't look at each other. Both of us looked straight ahead.

You ask what we talked about. I can't tell you. We hardly talked at all. It was all so completely different from what I had imagined. She said, "I'm glad that you came." I said, "Thank you for your letter."

I really wanted to say something completely different. I wanted to reproach her and to defend myself. But it was as if it were blown away in her presence.

We were just silent. I don't know how long. Time flew. You understand — we weren't silent out of stubbornness. We were silent together. I could almost say, the silence welded us together.

How easily and how often I used to say to a girl, "I love you", and I wanted only to possess her and amuse myself. Now for the first time I should have said it and I couldn't. It was just as if the words were too small, too worn out, to say what the heart was thinking.

We didn't talk, and yet we did talk. Without words

both of us knew we loved each other. This certainty bored itself deeper and deeper into our hearts, like a sweet pain, like a great joy.

It was the most beautiful hour of my life. No-one should ever take the word "love" in his mouth without having experienced such an hour. It was as if we had known each other always, had always belonged together. It seemed to both of us as if we were one and the same person: she a part of me, I a part of her.

Suddenly I knew for sure: nothing could separate us any longer, no law or custom, no father or mother, no state or church.

Then I remembered that we were in a church. I thought, we are both standing before God, and we are making a promise to each other for life. I took her hand and for a long time our hands lay together, quietly and firmly.

Now I ask you, what is still lacking? Isn't that everything? Are we not married now? When does marriage begin? Does it really begin with the wedding? Doesn't it begin with the engagement, when we promise to each other, I will belong to you all my life? We have already made that promise before God. Hasn't our marriage already begun?

I can't even remember now about the farewell. It was as if I was dreaming. She asked me to come again soon, and I said that I was looking for work. Then we left the church one after the other, and went in different directions.

F.

Dear François,

I couldn't sleep all night, and I cried. I scolded myself because I didn't talk to you. My heart was so full. I wanted to tell you so much and I couldn't. Now you probably think that I am indifferent to you, that I don't care.

Please understand that I couldn't speak because I was so happy that you had come. I have no one but you.

Cecile

Dear Cecile,

Don't cry, Cecile, please don't cry. I understand you, understand you deeply. No, you don't need to be afraid. You need never be afraid when I am with you.

It was all my fault. I should have talked; I should have asked you something. But I couldn't either.

It all surprised me so much: how you greeted me, just as a matter of course. How you had prepared everything.

Then you sat beside me, as if you were there just for me. That said more to me than all words.

You've cast a spell upon me . . . I have hope again. Today I helped my mother in the garden, instead of staring at the bamboo poles of the roof. She looked at me in amazement.

Your François

2 I LOVE A YOUNG MAN

Dear Francois,

. . . So you were in the Catholic Church! I told you that
Cecile would have a good idea. In Africa it is difficult
indeed for a young man to meet a girl! The Church ought
to be able to help with this difficulty.

I'm very thankful that you both have experienced this
hour, and I can well imagine what thoughts went through
your hearts. There are some white people, you know, who
do not believe that Africans know what love is!

Your questions are difficult. You really have a gift for
putting questions. They become harder all the time, and
I must think about them longer before I can answer them.

When does marriage begin? The Bible says that
marriage is a mystery. You cannot explain a mystery.
You can only keep penetrating a mystery. You never get
to the end of it. The beginning also belongs to the mystery.

You write: "It seemed to both of us as if we were
one and the same person." When does a person begin?
As far as the public is concerned, only from the time of
its birth. But life is certainly there before that. When
does life begin? Biology says: life begins at the moment
of conception.

From that moment on, life is there. A new person has
begun. And yet this person cannot be seen. It is in an
in-between stage while the mother carries it in her womb.
One can only say: a new person is on the way.

That is a picture of engagement and marriage. Your life
together has truly begun. Did it really begin in that hour
you were together in the church? Wasn't it there already

before that? Did it start when you first met in the bus? Or sometime during those weeks of the first ardent correspondence? Who can say? It remains a mystery.

From now on this new person, this new living being which you together make up, is on the way.

But this being on the way needs time. This new person must grow slowly, just as a child grows in his mother's womb. This growing together slowly will take place during the time of engagement. All that you experience leads to this growth: the beautiful and the difficult; the joy of seeing one another again and the pain of the separation; the speaking and the silence; the writing of a letter and the waiting for an answer; hope and disappointment, yes even obstacles and difficulties. All that makes the new person, which you will become, grow and mature.

But this growth happens in secret. No one knows it, only you two and God — and the few persons in whom you have confided.

So your marriage has begun and yet it is not to be seen. It is like the little one in its mother's womb between conception and birth. You are at the in-between stage. Your marriage is on the way.

The wedding day will be the birth-day of your marriage. That is when the new person appears to the world. Then everyone can see it. Then a festival takes place. Then it is made known to everyone.

At the time of engagement you say to one another: "We want to try and see whether we belong together." On the wedding day you say openly in front of everyone: "We have passed the test and it has turned out positively."

Naturally marriage does not come into being through the marriage certificate, any more than a child comes into being through the birth certificate. But still you must not under-estimate these things. Marriage is not only a private matter. The official registration also belongs to it. Marriage exists in its fullest state when everybody can see it. At that time it is also protected legally. Luther said once: "A secret marriage is no marriage." That is why the wedding has been celebrated, through all ages and by all peoples, by a feast.

Please believe me when I say that I can hardly wait to experience this birth-day of your marriage with you. I will gladly do everything that I can, so that it will be soon. That is why I wrote lately to Pastor Amos. But I have not yet received an answer.

T.

B. . . . ., September 20

Dear Pastor Trobisch,

Your letter surprised me in many respects. It was the Mission which introduced church discipline to us in Africa, even though it isn't practised in the European and American churches.

As long as the missionaries put it into practice themselves there were no voices raised against it. Now that we African pastors practise it, you criticize it. Actually we are only doing what you taught us to do.

Would François have come to you and confessed his sin if someone hadn't betrayed him? If he would have done that, and if the affair had been known only to him and the girl, then I would say perhaps you are right.

But he was 'repentant' only when he was caught. That is why we have to prove him to see if his repentance is really sincere. Refusing the Lord's Supper to him for six months is just a proving time — no sign that he is not forgiven.

This is also a warning to all the others in the congregation. Through such an example they receive power to withstand temptations. If I had not placed François under church discipline, then I would have led many others into temptation. I don't dare to do that. I am responsible to keep the church pure. In 1 Corinthians 11 : 27 it says: "Whoever eats the bread or drinks the cup of the Lord in an unworthy manner will be guilty of profaning the body and blood of the Lord." The sin threatens not only the life of the individual but of the whole congregation.

That is why it is the duty of the Church to punish sin in front of the whole congregation. God also punishes sin in the Bible. David was punished after he confessed adultery with Uriah's wife: his son died. Ananias and Sapphira fell down dead because of a lie (Acts 5 : 1—11).

I know our African young men better than you do. It is very easy for them to confess something when by doing so they will escape punishment. Your way is very dangerous. If it is so cheap to get forgiveness that one needs only to come to you, and then everything is all right, then the temptation to sin again is great, instead of leaving the sin and fighting against it.

On the other hand, punishment leads to true repentance. If we had not punished François, then probably he would not have repented of his deed.

That is why I can't give him back his job in our school right away. All the teachers and the pupils know of his case. If he hadn't been dismissed, that would have undermined the school discipline.

Originally, cases of adultery were rare in African society. They were punished very severely, at times even with death. Missionaries through their preaching have made it to be the main sin, if not the only sin. Through that they have made it attractive. On the other hand they forbid us to punish it. What shall we do?

I gladly agree to your request, and will visit Cecile's family, though I already know with what arguments the father will defend himself. I would like to take François with me. Please ask him to visit me.

Pastor Amos

Y. . . . ., September 22

Dear François,

Your letter comforted me very much. I am happy that you are not angry with me. I wanted to write to you before. But we had so much homework to do.

I have good news for you. My friend Bertha has an

uncle who works in the Ministry of Education. She says he would like to give you a job as a teacher in one of the public schools in Y.

Please accept this offer. Then you can earn money and we can see each other every day.

Your Cecile

E. . . . ., September 24

Dear Pastor,

Thank you for your letter of September 19. I had to think it over for a long time. The comparison between the time of engagement and the time of pregnancy is interesting. But when a child is conceived, it is easy to work out roughly what the date of its birth will be. I can't work out when we may be able to be married. That is what makes the waiting so difficult.

Your letter came in the same mail with one from Cecile. I'm enclosing it. What do you say about it? Is it possible for me as a Christian to teach in a public school?

Do you think it is good for us both to be in the same city? I long for it. And yet I know already, I would miss Cecile's letters.

François

Dear François,

. . . Of course you can work in a public school as a Christian. If the Church could have given you a job, then it would have been right to take it. But Pastor Amos wrote to me that under the present circumstances it would be impossible. We must see his reasons. He also makes his decisions after thought and prayer.

For you that means the way is free. God leads us step by step, just as He promises us only our daily bread, and not our whole livelihood.

My advice is this: accept the position in Y. Perhaps your testimony can be even more effective when you live among non-Christians. Be on the alert, and keep your eyes open.

Also, for the sake of your future marriage, it is good to see each other often. I wrote to you before that your engagement time should be a time of preparation. Your life together has begun, but at present it is still being tested and proved. Not that you have to test Cecile, nor she you. But you both seek together to know whether before God you can become one in spirit.

For that purpose letters are often very helpful, because you can write many things which are hard to say. But you cannot really get to know each other just through letters. You must meet one another in different situations, in good and bad moods. You need to talk together so that you can get to know each other fully.

Being silent is part of the conversation. You have

experienced that already. But it is only a part. Now you must also find words. You must find out if you can talk to each other and can also listen to each other. A marriage without plenty of talk is like a plant without sap. One day it will dry up.

It isn't necessary for you always to have the same opinion. But you must love each other so much that you will value each other's opinions.

One thing will become more difficult if you see each other every day: to draw the limits and to withstand temptation. When you are together, then remember that your mother was once a girl too.

I remind you of everything that I told you at the beginning of the year about becoming a man and about self-control.[2] Self-control is vital for the happiness of your marriage. But it will be possible in marriage only if it is learned and practised before marriage.

One more thing: Pastor Amos wrote to me that he will visit Cecile's father and that he would like you to go with him. On your way to Y. please stop at his house and fix a date for this. I will think about you specially on that day.

T.

[2] See, I LOVED A GIRL . . . page 17

B. . . . ., September 28

Dear Pastor Amos, T. defends F

Your letter, dear Brother Amos, is very matter-of-fact, almost cold. That is how I know that my last letter hit you very hard, and I can feel how hard it was for you to answer me at all.

Thank you all the more for writing to me, and especially for writing so frankly and honestly.

Yes, we missionaries have made mistakes. We must regret many things we have done. I've written the same thing to François, in whose life story the Mission is not without blame.

The miracle is that, in spite of our mistakes, God has built a church. To Him alone be the glory!

I would not defend myself, if it were for my sake. But it is for the sake of François and for so many others who are in his position. For their sakes we must seek to find what is the will of God. Please believe me, this was why I asked certain questions.

Is there really any human way by which we can determine the sincerity of repentance? Is it a proof of true repentance if one lets go of a certain sin for a certain time? Is it not God alone who can see into the heart?

You quote 1 Corinthians 11. There it says: "Let a man examine himself" (verse 28). Isn't that exactly the opposite of what we practise in the African churches, where it is the pastor and elders of a congregation who examine the members? And even if that were commanded, why should not the pastors and missionaries also be examined?

Who is "worthy" at all? Am I? Are you? If only the worthy ones were permitted to go to Communion, who would dare to go? Only those who are conscious of their unworthiness are really worthy to attend.

It is this truth which François has discovered and now knows more deeply and more clearly than ever. That is why he looks for and needs the fellowship of Jesus. As men then, do we dare to stand between him and his Lord? Do we dare to withhold from him that which Christ wishes to give him?

Yes, I admit: God does punish. But in all the examples which you give it is always God who punishes, not men, not the Church. Nathan, David's counsellor, did not punish David. Besides, we must never forget that David lived before Christ died on the cross. We who live after the time of Christ have the promise of Isaiah 53 : 5: "He was wounded for our transgressions, he was bruised for our iniquities; the chastisement of our peace was upon him; and with his stripes we are healed." Christ took the punishment which we have deserved, and suffered in our place. That is why, if we have confessed our sins and believe in Him, we can go out free.

Isn't that the message which God has entrusted to His Church, this free offer of grace without cost? The grace which God offers to us is certainly not cheap. It is costly. It cost Christ His life. But this is what is beyond understanding: this costly grace is offered to us entirely free.

You say: that is dangerous; that can be abused. Certainly; you are entirely right. It is often abused. But it is God Himself who has made this dangerous offer. If God dared to do it, should we put up our human walls of protection by means of church discipline?

Dear Brother Amos, you have put a serious question before us pastors. Is it not a lack of faith which stands behind church discipline? Do we not believe that God Himself can keep His Church pure? Do we think we have to do something on our own? Are we really responsible to keep the Church pure? Isn't it much more our task to announce the message, the gospel, the offer of grace, without any strings attached. If we obey God in doing that, then He will certainly do His part.

The example of Ananias and Sapphira which you cite, is a proof that He actually does that. This couple did not confess. They lied. They both fell dead on the spot. That's how hard God can be. Once more — Peter did not do that. God Himself stepped in. And He still does it today. Do we believe that? Do we have confidence in Him to do it?

And now one last question: Do you really think that it is so simple and easy to confess your sins? That's what those who have never done it often say. For me it was the hardest step that I ever took. Also for François. He had a hard battle with himself. I can testify to that. A counsellor can feel it.

I can understand what you write about school discipline. Certainly a school is not a church. I don't think it would be good for François to go back to the same school. But maybe there is another solution.

I have already written to François that he should look you up. Thank you very much for your readiness to go with him to Cecile's father. May God give you much wisdom for this visit. I will think about you specially on that day.

Walter T.

Y. . . . ., October 17

Dear Pastor,

I have been in Y. now for two weeks. No, almost three weeks. How the time flies!

On the way here I visited Pastor Amos. He was very friendly to me. I was really surprised. Tomorrow we will go together to Cecile's father. My half-brother Jaeques will come with us as the representative of our family. So it will be an "official" visit.

But before I go there I want to send you a few lines. Cecile has actually succeeded in finding work for me. I am grateful to Cecile every morning at 8 when I enter school. But I am still more grateful each evening at 5 when I can see her.

Cecile is a genius. She always has new ideas. She has borrowed two bicycles. With these we can ride out every day after school is over until it gets dark. Then she has to go home to her uncle.

Yes, and now we are "discovering" each other, as you would express it. Each day is full of new discoveries. A girl is certainly unknown territory. Now for the first time I see how blind I was when I considered a girl as I would a tooth-brush — something which one uses. And I wanted to "use" one in order to know how a "woman" is — oh!

Now I want to get to know only one girl — and that girl is called Cecile. It is as if all the others no longer exist. In her I get to know all girls, all women . . .

I let her ride ahead of me so that I can see her. She has her hair fastened up on her head, so I can see her long slender neck. I dreamt of it the other night. When we go up a hill she has to exert herself and pushes harder on the pedals. Then her beautiful neck moves in rhythm with her body. I could watch this for hours.

Then we get off our bicycles and sit in the grass. There's hardly a topic that we haven't already talked about. She has her own opinion about everything. I didn't know that a girl could think, let alone have her own opinion.

What she says isn't nearly as important to me as the fact that she says something and how she says it. I listen then to the sound of her voice, watch her hands and her eyes.

Then I would like to touch her. You wrote to me once: "Keep your caresses for your fiancée." But Cecile now is my fiancée. How far do I dare to go? You advised me to keep within the limits. But what is the limit?

Oh, I'll tell you right away: we kiss. That far it always goes. Not right away. At first we both feel a little strange. Each time we have to get re-acquainted. But while we talk, our hands look for each other. I can tell that she is waiting until I take hold of her hand, her arm. She is even pleased when I lean her head on my shoulder. She smiles a little, is very quiet, as if she just tolerates it. Then comes the kiss.

Is that going too far? Can we do that as Christians? What if our church elders should see us!

I must confide something else to you. When I kiss her, then the desire arises within me to possess her completely. I can't hinder it.

If you had not reminded me of my own mother, that she too was once a girl; if Cecile had not written to me once: "I loved you even more because in that first night you didn't come to me", I don't know what would have happened already.

When I dedicated myself to Christ that night at your home, I thought that I was set free. You said then, "Christ is not a nothing. He is a power. Through His power you can overcome."

At first it seemed that way. But now I see that it is not true. The desire ist stronger than ever. My faith doesn't help me. Christ doesn't hear my prayers. They fall into emptiness. The desire is stronger than Christ. Why doesn't Christ help me, do something to me, so that I can be finished with this desire, this craving to possess a girl — once and for all.

The experience of love destroys my faith. Or must one who believes flee from love?

I'm afraid. Afraid of myself. Afraid of the animal which sleeps within me.

Do you understand? This letter is a cry for help.

Tomorrow I am going on a trip. When I return after two or three days, there must be a letter from you. Otherwise there might be a disaster.

François

Dear François,

It is almost midnight. But I want to answer your letter right away.

You write that Christ hasn't heard your prayer. I ask you, what did you pray for? That He would deliver you from being a man? What do you want? To be without sex? To have no more desire at all?

There isn't any such thing. All that one does, one does either as a man or woman. Your sexuality is in your waking and sleeping. It is present with you when you work and when you play. In your holiest feelings and in your purest prayers it is there.

If you believe in Christ, then you know that your body has become the temple of the Holy Spirit. If you pray for the mutilation of the temple, then Christ will not hear you. Christ wants to make you capable of living with your manhood.

Must the one who believes flee from love? I know there are many Christians who withdraw themselves and who turn their backs on it. They avoid the opposite sex and think by doing so that they are especially mature and redeemed Christians.

They fool themselves. He who believes does not flee.

Christ did not evade this issue. He came into this world. He was a young man. He came into touch with women's hands, women's kisses, women's tears.

He came to the bedside of a sick woman. He took a young girl by the hand. A woman touched His robe. Two women who loved Him are called by their names, Mary and Martha. He spoke with women alone, once at the well and another time writing in the sand. The sinner who kissed His feet was a woman of bad reputation. Those in the room were shocked. Yet He defended her. He moved among people in a free and natural way.

He is the one who has overcome because He lived the life of a human being. To overcome means to be on the way to mastery. He will lead you to that goal, not to flight.

You can't run away from your manhood: it belongs to you; it is a part of yourself.

Let me tell you a story:

Once upon a time there was a tiger. He was captured and put in a cage. The keeper's task was to feed him and guard him.

But the keeper wanted to make the tiger his friend. He always spoke to him in a friendly voice whenever he came to his cage. The tiger however always looked at him with hostility in his green glowing eyes. He followed every movement of the keeper, ready to spring on him.

The keeper was afraid of the tiger and asked God to tame him.

One evening, when the keeper had already gone to bed, a little girl got lost in the vicinity of the tiger's cage and came too near to the iron bars. The tiger reached out with his claws. There was a blow, a scream. When the keeper arrived he found dismembered human flesh and blood.

Then the keeper knew that God had not tamed the

tiger. His fear grew. He drove the tiger into a dark hole where no one could come close to him.

Now the tiger roared day and night. The terrible sound disturbed the keeper so that he could no longer sleep. It reminded him of his guilt. Always in his dreams he saw the torn body of the little girl. Then he cried out in his misery. He prayed to God that the tiger might die.

God answered him, but the answer was different from what the keeper had expected. God said, "Let the tiger into your house, into the rooms where you live, even into your most beautiful room."

The keeper had no fear of death. He would rather die than go on hearing the roar of the tiger. So he obeyed. He opened the door of the cage and prayed: "Thy will be done."

The tiger came out and stood still. They looked into each other's eyes for a long time. As soon as the tiger noticed that the keeper had no fear and that he breathed quietly, he lay down at his feet.

That is the way it began. But at night the tiger would begin to roar again, and the keeper would be afraid. So he had to let the tiger come into his house and face him. Again he had to look the tiger directly in the eye. Again and again. Every morning.

He never had the tiger completely in his power "once and for all". Again and again he had to overcome him. Every day brought the same test of courage.

After some years the two became good friends. The keeper could touch the tiger, even put his hand between his jaws. But he never dared to take his eyes off the tiger.

When they looked at each other, they recognized each other and were glad that they belonged together and that each was necessary to the other.

François, you have to learn to live with the tiger, courageously, eye to eye. For that purpose Christ will set you free.

If you believe in Him, then you can dare to be tender to each other. There are Christians who think that God is especially pleased with them if they deny themselves this. But that is nonsense. Only he who truly believes can also really love.

How far do I dare to go? How far? As far as you can. Put your hand in the jaws of the tiger if you can.

But don't over-estimate yourself and don't skip over any of the steps. You must learn to feel which caresses are right for the particular occasion. Please don't think, just because many do it so quickly and easily, that kissing is not an art.

Never take your eye off the tiger. He is awake and prowling. He follows every movement, knows every weakness.

François, I am sending you along a dangerous road. But I don't want you to be evasive. Once more: He who believes does not flee.

I will give this letter tomorrow morning — no, this morning, because it was midnight long ago — to one of my friends who is going to Y., so that it will reach you quickly.

T.

Dear Brother Walter,

I want to tell you about our visit to Cecile's father.

But first, thank you for your letter of September 19. It did me a lot of good to hear from the mouth of a white man, even that of a missionary, that the whites are not without fault.

The sentence that God can build the Church even in spite of us when we fail, has comforted me greatly.

As far as church discipline is concerned, the question for me is always this: is there forgiveness without punishment?

Even the heathen believe that God punishes when His commandments are broken.

Then the missionaries came and said: God does not punish, rather God forgives. The result is that wherever Christianity has advanced, indiscipline breaks out. The heathen fear God, the Christians don't. They say: God doesn't punish, God forgives. So I don't risk anything if I sin.

What are we able to do then? I don't dare to act as you suggest. Perhaps I lack faith. Perhaps you Europeans have more faith than we do. Do your congregations really live more obediently than our congregations? Or do you just shut your eyes because you don't want to see sin?

For us Africans, when sin happens it hurts not only the individual but the whole community. In this way I believe we are closer to the thinking of the Bible than you are. You didn't go into this point.

This is also the vital point in the marriage palaver about Cecile. For her father, the marriage of his daughter is not only an affair between Cecile and François. It concerns the whole family. It isn't he who sets the bride-price. His brothers and above all the brothers and father of Cecile's mother set the price with him.

He has nothing personal against François. He thinks he is a decent and honest young man. But this is how Cecile's father is placed.

His first wife bore him no child. He felt however that he must have a son. He was convinced that he owed his father this debt: to pass on the life which he received from him. Otherwise his own life would not make sense.

So he took a second wife. She bore him Cecile and then shortly after that three sons.

It is true that he is certainly not one of the poorest in his village. He is a very industrious man who has a large cocoa plantation. But in spite of that, up till now he has only been able to pay half of the bride-price for Cecile's mother. The other half has to come out of the bride-price for Cecile.

Besides that he has three sons whom he wishes to send to school. The cost of tuition rises from year to year. And one day these three sons will want to marry also. But he has only one daughter for these three sons.

He is not just wanting to be rich, nor is he lazy; it is rather that he is very conscious of his responsibility. Cecile's uncles on her mother's side also keep their eyes on him.

We talked together quietly. He feels that a woman is

more obedient to her husband if he has paid something for her. Otherwise it would be easy for her to run away whenever there was a dispute, and say: "I don't belong to you, because you paid nothing for me." Also the husband, he says, remains more faithful to his wife if she has cost him something. In earlier times the bride-price was paid in cattle. If the marriage broke up, the cattle would have to be given back. So that helped to keep marriages together.

By introducing money into the country, the Europeans have destroyed this custom — that's what Cecile's father thinks. Behind it is also a reproach against me, because I have let myself become like a European. He doesn't say it outright, but I know it.

For him the bride-price is an honourable African custom through which the son-in-law shows the bride's father his gratitude and proves to him at the same time that he is capable of taking care of a wife.

There is another reason for the large amount of money he asks. My guess is that he is thinking about taking a third wife. He didn't say that to me, but I suspect it. The birth of the three sons, coming so quickly after each other, has made Cecile's mother very weak. Polygamy makes it possible to avoid that situation. The Church says: polygamy is sin; but it does not tell us how to space the children.

We ask ourselves sometimes how the missionaries solve this problem. But they always keep silent on this subject.

Now you can understand how it looks from the other side. What should I say? I don't know myself how I should be able to pay for the education of my sons if I gave away my daughter without a bride-price.

Cecile's father doesn't understand what love is. How shall I explain that to him?

You will certainly be disappointed and will think that I as an African could have done more than I did. That may be true. He certainly told me more than he would have told you. But there are also disadvantages.

Cecile's father and I — we are from the same clan. So we are distantly related. That hinders me, because I am too involved myself. In such a case perhaps you as a European could do more than I. You are neutral. You come from the outside. You could try . . .

I was very happy about François. He was modest and didn't try to push himself forward. But he will have to wait until he has more money. I don't see any other solution.

Pastor Amos

B. . . . ., October 26

Dear Cecile,

François will have told you how the visit to your father turned out. I received a detailed letter about it from Pastor Amos.

Cecile, please don't lose courage. God is with us, even in the darkness. True faith begins there, where one doesn't see at all. When all else forsakes us, all human hope, all hope of a solution, then there is only one thing left for us to do: to let ourselves fall into God's arms. God is never closer to us than in such moments. "Fear not, *only believe*", the Bible commands. We are only fully in God's hands when we have Him alone.

"*Only believe*"! That is something which must be learned. You and François must learn it together now. Nothing can prepare you better for your future marriage. That is why God sends you now into this darkness, takes away all supports upon which you could lean. So that you can learn and practise together to put your confidence in God *alone*.

How can you learn it? First of all: let God speak to you and listen to Him. When you are together, then open up your Bibles and read a portion together. Talk about it — what He says to you. Allow yourselves to be comforted, counselled and guided by God.

Then fold your hands together and spread out your worries before God. He knows the way. He will take you by the hand and lead you. He has brought you together. He will hinder the attempt of people to separate you. Believe that with all your hearts.

Don't be embarrassed to pray in front of one another. You will have to overcome this feeling of embarrassment. Now is your chance to learn it. Now you will see if you can talk about everything — also about your faith. A common faith is the most solid foundation for a marriage. If you build your house on this rock, then no storm can destroy it.

I talked for a long time yesterday with Ingrid about what could be done in your case.

First of all, we suggest that you write a letter of thanks to Pastor Amos. He is a good shepherd. It is touching that the old man undertook such a long and difficult trip. We respect him greatly.

And now we have a favour to ask of you, Cecile. That is the reason I write to you, although the letter is meant for both of you.

From your letter of July 19, written to François, it was clear that God has given you the gift of writing good letters. Now we ask you, would you consider writing your father a letter? We know that this is something very unusual for an African girl. Perhaps that is why it could be effective.

Two things seem hopeful to us in Pastor Amos's account. In one place he writes about your father: "He has nothing personal against François." And then: "He doesn't understand what love is."

Cecile, try to explain to your father what your love for François is — to give him a feeling of it. We often reproach fathers because they do not talk to their daughters. Perhaps it is rather the opposite: the daughters do not speak to their fathers. They do not tell them what they feel, what they suffer and what they hope.

Write this letter in your mother tongue. Write that you love your father, that you understand him, and that you don't want to leave him in the lurch.

Give him some practical suggestions. You will think of something. Of course François must be in accord with such suggestions. In that way you can try out something else: whether or not you can plan your finances together.

It is not enough during the time of your engagement just to see whether you understand each other, whether you can be tender to each other, whether you can believe and pray together. You must also see if you have the same attitude towards money, so that you can decide together about what you spend. A wife should know how much her husband earns, and you must be in agreement as to how you will spend your money.

Your attitude towards money is much more important than how much money you have.

One other thing, Cecile, which I tell you in confidence. At the beginning of the year, even before he met you, I wrote to François, "You are responsible before God for the girl."

Now I write the same thing to you. You, a girl, determine how far François can go. No young man can go further than the girl allows. Don't have any false pity. Be a queen. You love a young man. Make him a mature young man.

T.

Y. . . . ., November 1

Dear Pastor and Madame,

Thank you very much for your letter. I read it to François and we were both very moved to know you can put yourselves in our situation, that you feel exactly as we feel and that you want to comfort us.

We didn't know that God cared so much about us, that faith had anything to do with engagement. Without faith, we would have to give up now. But just because we do not know what the future holds, we feel even more closely bound together.

We have tried for the first time to read the Bible together. At first it seemed very strange. But then it was wholesome. It helps us if we are not only tender to one another, but if we are doing something else together. But we haven't prayed together yet. I'm ashamed to pray aloud in front of François.

I have tried to write to my father, but it just doesn't work. I can't tell you how hard it is for me. As a European I don't think you can understand it. It is as if there is a wall which separates me from my father.

Our fathers do not like to hear their daughters speak to them. They are afraid they will lose their authority. They think we do not respect them and they are offended.

I know that you meant your suggestion well. I have begun a letter and will try to continue it. Every line is a battle. It is so hard to put into words what I feel.

But even if I write it, I know I will never have the courage to send the letter.

Cecile

Dear Pastor Walter,

I am glad that your letter was here when I got back from that fruitless trip to Cecile's father. I was completely disheartened and desperate. But when I saw the envelope with your writing on it, it gave me fresh courage. It was just as if you had reached our your good, strong hand to me. Even before I opened the letter I was comforted.

I thought: what happens to all those who don't have anyone to whom they can write a letter, no one who answers them . . .?

The story about the tiger is not bad. It shows me that neither those who put the tiger in a cage nor those who let him free are doing the right thing. The ones who follow the world are just as cowardly as those who are superpious. We mustn't give up the fight. It is not the fault of the tiger if we fall. It is up to me whether the tiger is my enemy or my friend. I have understood all that.

But there is still one question unanswered. What does it mean "to put your hand in the tiger's jaws"? Does that mean that I can go to the end if I am master of myself, quiet, and "don't skip any of the steps" as you say? Does this mean that we can become united bodily?

I asked you this question once before. Then it was about a girl I didn't care about, I didn't wish to marry, and whom I hardly knew. Do you remember?

I said then that I wanted to prepare myself for marriage. And you answered: On the contrary! You are learning habits which will disturb your marriage later on.

I said I had to take a girl now and then in order not to be ill. You answered again: On the contrary. You risk your health by doing that.

I said I wanted to prove that I was a man. You answered the third time: On the contrary, you are a dish-cloth.

You convinced me then. But you didn't go into one argument: that of true love!

What if one wishes to be united out of love? If it only concerned some girl on the streets, I grant you are right. But with one's fiancée? With the girl that you love, with whom you feel completely one, to whom you have made a promise for life? Why should one stop there just with caresses, when you can say, in the deepest sense of the word, that you belong together?

You said that you can never try out being with just any girl in this intimate way. I agree. But can't you try it out with your own fiancée? If engagement time is supposed to be a trial time, why shouldn't you try out *that* also? Would you say that also is "adultery", if an engaged couple should give themselves completely to each other?

I heard a pastor say once: "Marriage is a garden in which everything is allowed. Outside of the garden, everything is forbidden." Yes, and then suddenly on my wedding day, I am expected to be a perfect husband? How can you imagine that would be possible?

Please understand me rightly: I am not asking the right to spend the night with just any girl off the street. I'm talking about Cecile, whom I am going to marry.

Do we really need first a note of permission from the registrar's office, or from the church, in order to be united physically? Inwardly we feel already as much man and wife as we would after the wedding.

Sometimes I have the impression that Cecile waits secretly for the moment when she can belong to me completely. I have a friend who had already paid half the bride-price. But he didn't wish to sleep with his fiancée before the wedding. One day he received the money back from the girl's family. The family was afraid that he was impotent. I wonder sometimes whether Cecile suspects this when I do not take her. Perhaps she even thinks that I don't really love her?

Recently she stretched out in the grass. Just lay there. Gazing up into the sky. Completely innocent. Her dress was tight across her breasts, and her knees were uncovered. I just couldn't hold back any longer, and I took her in my arms with all my strength. But she broke away from me and ran to the place where our bicycles were standing. We didn't say a word all the way home, nor did we talk about it the next day.

How long can this continue? How long must we keep ourselves from each other? If only the end were in sight! But we have no hope that in the next four, five or even ten years someone will give us a licence.

Shall we run away? Where to?

François

Dear François,

A Christian is one who can wait. Someone gave this to me as a word of advice. I pass it on to you. Wait for the complete union. By not waiting you will gain nothing and you will lose much. I will put what you would lose in three words: freedom, joy and beauty.

You would lose freedom:

Let me tell you about another couple I know. They too thought that they loved each other and that they felt inwardly already as man and wife. But after six months they noticed that they had made a mistake. They talked openly about their feelings and agreed mutually to break their engagement. It all happened very peacefully. No scars remained.

If they had given themselves to each other completely, that would not have been possible. I know that your feeling for Cecile is so much deeper that it could not be compared to your feeling for that girl at the beginning of the year. And that is just the reason why I advise you to wait. The deeper your feeling is for each other, the more lasting would be the wounds in case of a separation.

I have heard men who have been married for years say to their wives: "I knew before the wedding that I had made a mistake. But we had already gone so far that I didn't have the courage to break it off. Now I have to pay the price for my mistake."

I am glad to read in your letters how strong and true and overpowering is the love you are experiencing. Nevertheless feelings can deceive you. It takes a long time before you can really decide whether you sense something lasting. A recent survey in America has shown that in most of the happy marriages the partners have known each other for several years, and that they were engaged several months before their marriage.

A test is only genuine if it could turn out to be negative. The time of engagement is a time of testing only if there is the possibility of breaking the engagement. Breaking an engagement is an evil. It is painful. No one wishes it. But in comparison to a later divorce, it is certainly the lesser evil.

I will use the picture of a birth again in order to make clearer what the engagement means. If I compare marriage with a child which is ready to be born, then the time of engagement is the time before birth. A broken engagement would be then — using this picture — like a miscarriage, which is what happens when a child is not able to live. In the moment however that you come together a miscarriage is almost impossible. Then there is no returning. Then a separation would be like the murder of a child.

So you would lose your freedom. But even more: you would spoil the joy which the growing, the maturing and waiting brings with it.

A married woman, talking about her experience before marriage, put it once this way: "Everything went along fine for a while. But then there came an unexpected pregnancy. Plans had to be changed quickly and excuses had to be made. The wedding was celebrated hurriedly. Our married life began without romance and without dignity. It didn't pay."

A premature birth endangers the life of the child. Of course, many children survive a premature birth. But never without difficulty.

When Cecile ran away from your sudden embrace, she just reacted naturally and without long reflection. Her healthy, unspoiled instinct protected her. She felt that the time was not yet ripe, that your happiness would be put in danger through this step. Actually your harmony was also broken and you didn't speak to each other any more that day.

I do not really believe that Cecile doubts your love when you restrain yourself. It is much more possible that her love grows. Your being together is still in a hidden stage. It is right also at this stage that you have not completely revealed or unveiled yourselves to each other. On your wedding day a piece of undiscovered land should still lie before you.

Of course the sexual side of your marriage is very important. You know already that you are not impotent, and Cecile knows it too. If there were any doubts, then a doctor could confirm it. That is no reason for wounding Cecile's feelings nor for risking your happiness.

Sexual harmony cannot be tried out. Even an engaged couple cannot determine it reliably before the wedding. There are two conditions necessary and both of these can be found only after the wedding; unlimited time and being completely free from fear.

If Cecile has to say herself: "Today between 5 and

6 p. m. I must meet François. Then it must happen. Then I must be ready. Then it must succeed — otherwise he will leave me" — I can tell you now with certainty: these thoughts will check her and lame her, so that both of you will be disappointed.

Suppose you tried it out and it turned out negatively? Suppose it didn't work as you thought it should. Would you then say: we shall have to break our engagement? You don't believe that. Your love is not that superficial. It is already too deep. Why then do you want to experiment?

No one expects you to be a perfect married couple on your wedding day. There is no such thing as a perfect married couple. There is only a mutual growing towards perfection. Often it takes years before man and wife are really adjusted to each other. The unlimited time which you need for growth you will find only in marriage. All that you can do before marriage is to protect yourself from experiencing or learning things which will hinder you from growing.

You can't have your cake and eat it too. The magic and beauty of the engagement period lies in the fact that there still remains one last secret, there is still a room which will only be entered when the hour has come.

Just imagine that your father wants to surprise you with a bicycle for Christmas. He hides it carefully. But you take it secretly out of the hiding place and try it out. Then on Christmas Day you have to act as if you are surprised and joyful, but the holiday is colourless and empty.

Your wedding day and your first night will become more beautiful if you have waited. Not until that night will you understand me fully. The wedding is not a formality. If you have testified in public, before God and men: "We belong together", then the experience will be much deeper and it will have a much fuller meaning when you give yourselves to each other completely.

We tell our children in Europe a fairy-tale: "A king's daughter was put under a magic spell by a witch, and she had to sleep for 100 years until a prince would awaken her with a kiss. In order to protect the princess, there was a hedge of thorns which grew up all around the castle. All the princes who tried to break their way in before the 100 years were up were caught in this hedge and died. But for the prince who could wait, the thorns yielded and the way was free."

I can only put you into the hands of your heavenly Father. He will give you something beautiful. Let me say it again: "A Christian is one who can wait."

You won't be able to reach me by letter during these next few weeks. I have to make a trip to the North. But I hope to be back before Christmas.

T.

Dear Madame Ingrid,

I was so surprised when François introduced me to you yesterday after the service that I couldn't say anything. I'm sorry that you had to leave so quickly and that your husband wasn't with you. How much I would like to get to know him also!

I wanted to write to you before. But now that we've seen each other it will be easier for me. Strange, but I just can't write to my father. I've already made many notes of what I want to tell him; I've begun the letter but again and again I've had to stop. A letter just won't come out of it all.

Still, I have the feeling that you will understand me. You probably think that I am very happy, and I am. Just the same my heart is often heavy. I have doubts, and I'm afraid.

I have doubts about whether François really loves me. He never tells me that he does. He often asks me if I love him, and he can't hear my answer often enough. But he never says that he loves me. Then doubts arise in my heart. I can only love him if I can answer to his love. He seems to think it isn't necessary to tell me that he loves me, and why he loves me. How can I answer him then? He makes me so uncertain. How can you test love?

Your husband has written to François the story about the princess. I wonder what the prince did after he had awakened the princess. Was he not very careful, very tender, so that she wouldn't be afraid? Did he not tell her how much he loved her, and why?

Just lately we had a quarrel. It was about something very trivial and ridiculous. I had a flat tyre on one of our daily bicycle rides. I had a repair kit and François mended the tyre. That made him bad-tempered — and me too — because of the time we had lost. When he had finished, we discovered that I had left the pump at home. I always take it off, to prevent it being stolen. Then he started to scold me, and said it just proved that girls have no intelligence. I was hurt because he was so rude, and out of stubbornness I didn't say a single word while we pushed our bicycles home. It was nothing serious at all. The next day we made it up again. But I ask myself — if we have quarrels already, what will it be like later on?

And then I'm afraid. I would like to be sure whether I can bear a child or not. I'm afraid that François will divorce me if I'm barren. Or that he will take a second wife, like my father. Is there any justification for marriage if there is no child?

Then there is still another problem. Lately I received the enclosed letter from a certain Monsieur Henri. He is a brother of the uncle of my friend Bertha who helped François to get his job as a teacher in Y. This Monsieur Henri works in the Ministry of Finance and has a good position. He even wanted to pick me up in his car.

Of course I refused him. What shall I do if he invites me again? I don't want to be rude.

Please answer me!

Cecile

Dear Mademoiselle Cecile,

Your friend Bertha has told me about you. I would like
to make your worthy acquaintance, and shall be honoured
to wait for you in my car tomorrow at 5 p. m. outside
your school entrance.

Monsieur Henri

B. . . . ., November 18

Dear Cecile,

How well I understand you, my sister! I could show
you letters from the time of my engagement in which I
expressed the same anxieties and doubts.

But we also do not make it easy for the men, Cecile.
On the one hand we want a man to be strong, wise and
unsentimental. On the other hand we want him to be full
of feeling, to be tender and to need us. What man can
combine both of these wishes in a single person?

I will try to write directly to François. Don't ask him
about this letter, if he does not show it to you himself.
For you there is only one way — you must tell him frankly
and honestly when something is wrong, when you are
hurt. As long as you can do that then there is no danger
to your marriage.

One thing more: you cannot prove or measure the
quantity of love before marriage. It is not true that marriage
grows only out of love. The opposite is also true: love

grows out of marriage — sometimes very slowly. In the Old Testament story of Isaac and Rebecca it says: "Then Isaac brought Rebecca into the tent, and took her, and she became his wife; and he loved her" (Genesis 24). They married without having seen each other beforehand. The falling in love came afterwards.

Most of the marriages that you see around you were begun without any great personal love experience. Often the girls weren't even asked. You know yourself that they are not all unhappy. Often love has grown after the wedding as a fruit of the marriage.

An Indian once said to a European: "You marry the girl that you love. We love the woman that we have married." Another Indian put it even more drastically: "We put cold soup on the fire, and it becomes slowly warm. You put hot soup into a cold plate, and it becomes slowly cold." You'll have to decide yourself on which side you Africans belong.

I am writing in this way so that you will not overestimate the love experience. It is certainly important. But love will become fully mature only in the atmosphere of marriage.

It is not only good, it is even necessary to have some disagreements. My husband even hesitates to marry a couple who have never had a quarrel. What counts is not that you never quarrel, but that you can make it up again afterwards. That is an art which can and must be learned before marriage. As long as you are able to forgive each other you don't need to be worried about the future of your marriage.

The man who is not ready to be the first to apologize after a quarrel should not marry; and the man who has no humour had also better not marry. It is wonderfully wholesome if you can laugh about yourselves after a quarrel.

When you ran away from François, it was the thorn hedge in you which reacted — the thorn hedge which protects the sleeping princess. Many girls who give themselves too early never become mature. That is why it says three times in the Old Testament book, *The Song of Solomon:* "I adjure you . . . that you stir not up nor awaken love until it please." This entreaty stands as if it were written in flames above the door of marriage.

Perhaps the waiting will be easier if you don't see each other daily. Then each meeting will be more significant. There are no rules about this. You must find out what is best for the two of you.

How well I understand your wish — your heart's desire for the happiness of motherhood! But the most frequent cause of sterility is a venereal disease. That is why virgins have every chance of becoming mothers. But you can't be sure about God's will in this matter until you are married; then you receive the knowledge that you will become a mother as a gift from God. There is no other way.

But do not think that if you have a pregnancy before marriage, it can be compared with the deep happiness of motherhood! True, one problem is solved: you know that you can conceive a child. But many new problems arise. There is no home in which the little one can be born, no father who can carry the child on his arm. There will even be a dispute about who the child belongs to as long as the father has paid no bride-price. You will have to leave school and be made fun of and criticized by your teachers and class-mates. For the certainty that you gain, you must exchange feelings of shame and guilt, self-reproach and the loss of self-respect. It doesn't pay. The price is too high.

Or do you have the secret desire, through a pregnancy, to force your father to consent to the wedding? Please, please, I beg of you, don't do that! Don't lower your child to be a means by which you reach your own goal. God has another solution if you can wait.

Give all your anxieties about motherhood to God. Even if you should have no child, that is no ground for a divorce. Your husband also has no right to take a second wife if your marriage has been registered as a monogamous marriage.

A Christian marriage has meaning and purpose even if God should give no children to the couple. The Bible speaks about marriage only in a very few places. So it is all the more striking that the same verse is quoted four times: "Therefore a man leaves his father and his mother and cleaves to his wife, and they become one flesh" (Gen. 2 : 24; Matt. 19 : 15; Mark. 10 : 7; Eph. 5 : 31). Notice how in this key verse, repeated four times, there is no word about children. According to the Bible, children are an added blessing of God. But they are not the only reason for marriage. The love of the two partners for each other, the becoming-one-person of man and wife before God, is a meaning and fulfilment of marriage in itself.

It is serious about that Monsieur Henri! I don't like the sound of his letter. Be sure to talk it over with François, otherwise misunderstandings may arise. In no case and under no conditions accept an invitation from him!

Ingrid T.

B. . . . ., November 19

Dear François,

My husband is away on a trip and can't write to you at present. So I am writing you a letter today. I should like to talk to you as if I were your sister.

God has laid a great treasure in your hands: Cecile's love. I would like to help you guard this treasure in the right way.

Love is not something which you can own, something which you can put in your pocket. Love is something you must win anew — over and over again. During the time of our engagement, Walter once wrote these lines to me:

"He who loves is no more alone. For the one whom he loves is always present. The one who loves has no wish to remain the centre of his own life. He permits someone else to enter into the midst of it, and feels that is a great gain and happiness. He gives himself up and lets himself go. He becomes empty like an open hand which holds nothing, but waits until something is put into it. He who loves has the courage to become someone who needs something."

What Cecile needs above all else is the assurance that you need her. How can you give her this assurance? Only in this way — that you tell her over and over again, "I love you, I need you." She can't hear it often enough. You must have the courage to "become someone who needs something".

A girl becomes afraid if a young man simply takes her love for granted and never bothers even to tell her that he loves her.

Woman's love is different from mother love or sister love. Cecile's love can only blossom out to the fullest if it can be in answer to your own love.

The Apostle Paul wrote to the church in Ephesus: "Husbands, love your wives, as Christ loved the Church." We love Christ because He has first loved us. Our love is an echo of His overwhelming love. It is strange that Paul never admonished the women to love their husbands . . .

I am not thinking now about physical love. You will never convince Cecile of your love by your caresses, your embraces and kisses alone. She wants to feel that your heart is seeking her heart and that you mean her herself and not just the beauty of her body.

A young man *is* his body. Your body, that's you. A girl feels herself *in* her body. Cecile senses that her inner being is not revealed just in her outward beauty. She wants to be loved for her own sake and not just for the sake of her beauty.

That's why your caresses are much less important to Cecile than is your whole way of acting. If you are polite to her, help her to get on her bicycle, open a door for her and let her go ahead of you — all that can mean more to her than a kiss. A woman who has been married for many years told me once with a sigh, "If only my husband would say 'Thank you' just once, when I have prepared an especially good meal".

Above all, it hurts a girl if you are more polite to others than you are to her. Then she notices that you treat her as if she were a piece of property.

When we met recently after church, you were very polite to me. You introduced me to Cecile, it's true. But during our whole conversation you didn't give her a chance to say a word. I had brought her a parcel of books which she could read as a preparation for marriage. As you went away, you let her carry the parcel . . .

You laugh. You laugh? That's such a little thing, you say, very unimportant. For a girl's heart, it is a big thing. For Cecile it is a very important thing.

Don't be stingy with words. Give her courage so that she can tell you what bothers her, what she misses in you. Listen to her lovingly, not just patiently. The most important thing is not that you are happy, but that you make her happy; not that you are understood, but that you understand . . .

Ingrid T.

Dear Madame Ingrid,

. . . Your letter comforted me most when you wrote and said that you also have troubles, anxieties and doubts. The white people always try to give us the impression that their married lives are ideal and without problems. Then we read in the papers about the many divorces in Europe and America — and we can't understand how the two go together.

That's why your letter meant all the more to me. I feel that I can tell you everything. By the way, the letter to my father is almost finished. On many slips of paper. All the thoughts that I would like to say to him if only I could. But I can't. I just can't force myself to send the letter.

Monsieur Henri gives me no peace. Here is another of his letters. Almost every day I get such a letter with all those insignificant phrases. They sound as if he had copied them out of a cheap love novel.

Thanks for your clear advice. I have refused the invitation through my friend Bertha. I'd rather not write to him myself. I do not wish a letter from me to him even to exist.

Cecile

Dear Mademoiselle Cecile,

I am very sorry that you have no time for me. But my love for you grows from day to day. You are the crown of my heart. You are as beautiful as the moonlight.

I've already sent my brother to your father in K. He is in accord. I will send your father £75 soon. That's just a trifle for me. Then nothing will stand in the way of our happiness.

Next week there will be a big banquet for the high government officials. I would like to invite you to it. Your uncle will also attend.

You will be happy in our marriage. You can have servants and even earn money yourself. You can live like a white person. Our social life will only be in educated circles.

But love is most beautiful during the night.

Monsieur Henri

Y. . . . ., December 15

Dear Madame,

Two weeks of torture lie behind me. I've been waiting every day for a letter from you. But I know that you are alone with the children and that you have very little time before Christmas.

Monsieur Henri comes every day with his car to the school entrance. He follows us if we go out on our bicycles. He spies on us — where we go and what we do.

Recently I met him at my uncle's as I came home from school. Bertha's uncle was there too, the one who helped François to get his job. That's how I knew that everything was planned. Then we went to a cocktail party. Under this name the foreign embassies of the whole world introduce their so-called "civilization" to our society. My uncle with whom I live went too. We African girls can't refuse if our fathers command us to do something.

I didn't dance. But I couldn't avoid Monsieur Henri taking me home alone in his car. He said that he had decided to marry me. He said it in just that way. As if it would be a great favour on his part. He didn't even ask me what I thought about it.

He wanted to kiss me right away — just as one would bite into a banana. His breath smelled strongly of beer and liquor. It was repulsive.

He is twenty years older than I am, and he already has a wife and two children. He says she's uneducated, doesn't know French and refuses to live in the city. But since he has a position in the government he needs a wife in Y. whom he can present, who can receive guests and entertain them. That's why he chose me.

He made it clear that he can pay the bride-price for me. I would estimate that his salary is at least twenty times as much as François earns. He will visit my father and take all sorts of liquor and several cases of beer with him. He's already bought a radio for him and a sewing machine for my mother. He asked me what my brothers would like to have as gifts. I didn't answer him. I was glad that

I could get out of the car without being molested. But I wept the whole night.

Money! A capital investment in women! The rich can buy them. The poor can at best rent a girl for a few nights, and then only the kind of girl that nobody wants much anyway.

No! I made a big mistake. Money doesn't give us value. It lowers us. It makes us just merchandise. It makes us either prostitutes or second and third wives of a rich man. That is no honourable African custom. That is no thankoffering to the parents. It is simply the slave-trade.

If my father accepts money from Monsieur Henri I am lost. I shall be married to him. I shall just be Monsieur Henri's shop sign, his sign of business. Purpose of marriage: the wife is the salesman for the husband!

Of course, I've told François everything. If your husband wasn't away on a trip, he would have already written to him. François is again completely discouraged and has shrunk into himself, but I love him just that much more.

But what is the solution?

François thinks that if my father receives both money and gifts from Monsieur Henri, then here's only one thing for us to do — to run away.

What do you think about this solution? I need the answer quickly.

"He who believes doesn't flee . . ." That's right, but isn't it also flight if one is forced into a marriage and gives up the battle . . . gives up love . . .?

Cecile

Dear Pastor and Madame,

This is the first letter addressed to both of you. We are writing it together.

We ran away. The answer to Cecile's letter of December 15 didn't reach us in Y. before we left. We think that probably you would have advised us not to run away. But we hope just the same that you will understand us. We couldn't see any other way out.

We had heard the news that Cecile's father had accepted £75 from Monsieur Henri. You know what that means. From now on he has a legal right to Cecile. To run away was our only weapon.

We decided together to do it, and we want to bear all the consequences together — even the bad ones. The fact that the school vacation has just begun made it easier for us to prepare everything without arousing suspicion.

You wrote to us once that the wedding day would be the day on which the marriage is born. You wrote: "A premature birth is dangerous."

But aren't there also births which are overdue? Aren't they even more dangerous? And then the doctor has to intervene and sometimes he even has to perform a Caesarean section. He has to cut the child out of the mother's womb in order to save its life.

Our running away is like a Caesarean section.

We don't know what is going to happen — where we shall live, or what we shall live on.

We know only one thing: now we are man and wife.

We have left father and mother. We cleave to one another. We have become one flesh. Genesis 2 : 24 is fulfilled. For that we need no money, no civil wedding, no pastor. We need no tradition, no customs, no state and no church. We need no liquor, no paper and no singing.

We need only God. He will not forsake us. All others have forsaken us.

Our custom is no safeguard for marriage. It crushes marriage under its feet. It makes it possible to steal the bride by signing a cheque. Even the state supports the unmarried mother and the fatherless child. Those who want to marry must go empty-handed. The Church advises us to wait, but it doesn't help us when we do that. It does not help us, either, if we flee. No pastor would dare to receive us in his home.

You also haven't answered our last letters. We do not reproach you. We only ask that you do not reproach us, nor judge us. We would like to remain your children in the future.

Cecile is sick and lies in bed. She caught a bad cold the night we ran away. We had to go a long distance on foot. She sends special greetings to your children.

We are telling no one where we are, not even you. That is why you won't be able to write to us now. You can do only one thing — pray for us.

We believe that you will do this.

François and Cecile

To the reader

When I returned from my trip, I found the preceding letter. At first I was just as disappointed as you probably are now. I too was wishing for a happy ending. But this is no thought-up movie. Cecile and François are not fairy-tale characters. They are human beings of flesh and blood who live among us. I would do both you and them an injustice if I did not tell you everything just as it happened.

A happy ending might put us to sleep. Reality shakes us awake.

When we face reality we have to face difficult questions. Was it the will of God that Cecile and François ran away together? Were they obedient to God by living together as husband and wife? Is it true, as François claims, that they are now married in the full sense of the word? We can't evade these questions.

Humanly speaking, we must agree. They had no choice but to run away. I would even dare to say that it was a courageous step. How do we know whether Cecile could have escaped a forced marriage to Monsieur Henri in any other way? It was certainly not God's will for Cecile to marry Monsieur Henri. She would have been guilty before God if she had consented to it.

On the other hand, I could sense even by the tone of their last letter that they had troubled consciences. The open scorn which they expressed in some places in this letter made me realize that they were trying to drown an inner voice — a voice which told them that their living together at this time and under these circumstances was not according to God's will. They weren't ready to admit this right away — not even to themselves. But finally they knew: by choosing this way they too were guilty before God.

This feeling of guilt, which increased each day, weakened Cecile's physical strength so much that her cold developed into a serious case of pneumonia. She was so ill that at her own request she was taken to her village. François came and got me, and I spent an unforgettable week at her bedside.

For days we didn't know whether Cecile would live or not. Both she and François looked upon this sickness as a punishment. Not so much because they had run away, but because of the hurried consummation of their marriage. They accepted God's judgment. During these difficult hours their faith in Jesus Christ, who had given His life for their guilt, was their only comfort. When Cecile recovered, almost miraculously, they learned in a new way that all of us live by grace alone.

But why was there no other solution? Why was there no third way? Why was there no place to which they could flee for protection? Why didn't they have someone whom they could trust?

Would you have received them if they had knocked at your door? Would you be willing to be criticized publicly by offering refuge in your home to a young couple in such a situation? What about the hostility of their families that would fall on your head and might even cause you to lose your job? Would you risk it?

Are we willing to suffer for what we believe to be right and good? Isn't it easier to act against our consciences and to yield to a custom which we detest from the depths of our hearts?

By running away, Cecile and François have protested against such a cowardly attitude on our part — against the irresponsibility found in state, church and family. By doing this, they accuse all of us who just let things go on as they are, and who watch passively while people are driven daily to take such desperate steps all around us.

There are certain moments and situations where people take guilt upon themselves. God can even use these moments to open our eyes to our own guilt. But this guilt — our own and that of others — we are only able to carry because of the cross of Jesus Christ. Without the reality of that cross our life becomes impossible.

It is our fault that François and Cecile became guilty.

As far as I am concerned, I want to confess this. I too have failed. I ask François and Cecile to forgive me, because I didn't fight hard enough for them, nor did I seek earnestly enough God's guidance in their case. I'm sorry that I didn't take my trip at some other time, that I didn't go to see Cecile; nor did I take the trouble to visit Cecile's father in order to talk to him personally.

My wife feels guilty too. How was it possible, she wonders, that she let Cecile's letter remain unanswered for so long? Instead of taking François and Cecile by the hand and walking with them, my wife and I both feel as if we had only sent them radio messages from an aeroplane.

No, we do not judge them. As Christians we can only

do one thing: help them on their way through prayer and practical help.

As you can see, the way our young couple have chosen is leading them through deep valleys. Don't think for one minute that running away as they did is just an easy way to reach the goal quickly! No one is advised to take such a step unless it is absolutely necessary and all other means have failed.

However, this time of suffering together, of great struggle and anxiety, is a true preparation for their future marriage. Already they have learned that they did not become "one flesh" through their physical union alone, but that this biblical expression means something far more. When a child is born, delivered into the light of day, every one can then see that child. So also it is with a true marriage. The public, legal act belongs to the foundation of a marriage.

We hope that Cecile and François can soon be legally married. We are working towards that end. If you would like to help us, perhaps by writing a letter to Cecile's father, or even Monsieur Henri, we will be glad to forward these letters. In this way you could even become a co-author of the next volume.

We hope that in that next volume we shall be able to tell you how the wedding took place, which I am confident will soon happen. And I can tell you already that the following letter 'which I want to share with you' has had its effect, and made it possible to find a solution which may be helpful to you too.

It is the letter we have mentioned often before, which

Cecile wrote to her father. Not until she was desperately ill did François find the slips of paper upon which Cecile had made a rough copy of the letter. These were thoughts she had jotted down, often incomplete sentences. Much of it was corrected, crossed out, then put together afresh, and once more discarded. It was a moving testimony to the trouble this letter caused Cecile, and to the struggle of a daughter's heart to gain the understanding and love of her father.

I put it all together — just as one puts together the parts of a mosaic. I organized and completed it and then sent it on to Cecile's father. But its message I directed towards my own heart. If we understand it rightly, it is addressed to us all. That is why I'd like to ask you to pass on this letter. Copy it. Translate it into your mother tongue. Read it to all who will listen. Not only to the fathers, but also to those who will become fathers. And to the Messieurs Henri!

But above all, to the girls of Africa. May this letter give them courage for a great, positive revolution! If Cecile is heard, then there is hope. Let us listen to what she has to say:

Dear Papa,

I have never written a letter to you before. It's very hard for me. But it would be even harder for me to talk to you. That's why I ask you to read these lines as if I were talking to you.

I wish all the girls of Africa would go to their fathers with me and do what they have not so far dared to do: open their hearts. I am convinced that if they could find words they would say what I am trying to say now.

I want to tell you why I love François.

When I picture him in my mind I always think of him stretching out his hand to me. I trust this hand. It is as if François is walking a little ahead of me; but then he stands still, turns round and gives me his hand to help me over the hard places. Then I come very near to him and he comforts me.

He can comfort me so wonderfully because I can answer him when he talks to me. I can take hold of his hand, because I'm not afraid when he stretches it out to me. He doesn't use his strength to make me feel inferior. And yet when I need protection, I'm sure that he is stronger than I am. In his presence I don't mind being weak, because he does not make fun of me.

But he needs me too, and he's not ashamed to show it. Even though he is strong and manly, he can also be as helpless as a child. His strong hand can then become an open, empty hand. Then I know no greater happiness than to fill it.

That's what I mean when I say: I love François.

I know that you think I am a half-white when I write such things to you. You blame me for despising our African customs, because I want to marry the man I love and not one who is able to pay for me.

But the custom of bride-price is not exclusively African. They had it in Europe too, and even in Israel. Wherever men become Christian this custom disappears. I do not write to you as a Europeanized African but as a Christian African.

As a Christian I believe that God has created me. To Him alone I owe my life. No earthly father has ever paid God anything for his daughter. Therefore no earthly father has a right to make money out of her.

As a Christian I believe that Jesus Christ died for me. He has paid the only price that can be paid for me: His blood. Any other price is the price for a slave.

As a Christian I believe that the Holy Spirit guides me. But I cannot follow His guidance unless I can choose freely.

Because I have chosen François of my own accord, I shall be faithful to him. Do you really think that bride-price could hinder a wife from running away from her husband?

I have a girl friend whose father received £500 from the man who married her. She felt that if her body had such value she could also get something out of it for herself. So she gave herself to other men for money. There you have it. If bride-price is acceptable and decent, why not prostitution?

Or do you think that François would treat me better if he paid something for me? If that is the reason why he would take better care of me, I do not want to marry him; for then I would only be a thing to him. But I am a human being.

It is not true that money makes a wife more obedient and a husband more faithful. At most, money is a chain which has to serve as a substitute as long as there is no love. But you can break a chain. You can return money or goods. Love that has chosen freely is an unbreakable tie.

Dear Papa, please don't think that we are ungrateful. Both of us love you dearly. We know of the sacrifices you made for me, especially when you sent me to school. We know too about your financial difficulties. We do not want to leave you in the lurch.

All we ask is this: give us a start without debts! Allow us to found our own home! Then we can really help; then we can show you how grateful we really are.

François suggests that we take my three brothers into our home when they go to school in Y. Isn't that a greater proof of his love to me than giving you money which does not belong to him?

Dear Papa: give us a chance! Let us begin.

Marriage Guidance Service

In case the reader has personal questions, he is invited to write to Pastor Walter Trobisch or Mrs. Ingrid Trobisch at one of the following addresses. All letters will be treated confidentially.

Pastor Walter Trobisch
Mrs. Ingrid Trobisch

68 Mannheim	P. O. Box 1192	Yaoundé
Traitteurstr. 60	Kitwe	P. O. Box 1133
Germany	Zambia	Cameroun

Where To Get Help in Reading

First of all — in the Bible. Many important passages in it deal with love and marriage.

Old Testament

Adam and Eve; the institution of marriage	Gen. 1 : 26—30; 2 : 18—25
Isaac and Rebecca; the choice	Gen. 24
The forbidding of infidelity	Ex. 20 : 14—17
Boaz and Ruth; faithfulness rewarded	Ruth 2—4
David and Bathsheba; adultery and repentance	2 Sam. 11 : 1—12; 25
Ahab and Jezebel; a badly matched couple and a disastrous marriage	1 Kings 16 : 29—33; 22 2 Kings 9 : 20—37
Love and happiness	Psalm 128
Seduction and death	Prov. 5 : 15—23; 7 : 1—27
The perfect wife	Prov. 31 : 10—31
Foolish women	Isa. 3 : 16—4 : 1
Love strong as death	Song of Sol. 8 : 6—7

New Testament

One flesh; the forbidding of divorce	Mark. 10 : 1—12
To love as Christ loved	Eph. 5 : 21—33
I am thine, thou art mine	1 Cor. 7 : 1—5
To remain single	Matt. 19 : 10—12
Irregularities and disorders	Rom. 1 : 18—32; 1 Cor. 5 : 1—5
Covetousness and adultery	Matt. 5 : 27—30
Love which forgives	John 8 : 1—11
The Great Yes to love	Matt. 22 : 34—40
Love, first fruit of the Spirit	Gal. 5 : 22
Love, the still more excellent way	1 Cor. 13
God is love	1 John 4 : 7—16

To Help You Further in Your Reading

THEODOR BOVET:
A Handbook to Marriage, Doubleday, New York

KENNETH G. GREET:
Guide to Loving, Hutchinson, London

L. J. TIZARD:
Guide To Marriage, Allen and Unwin, London

DAVID MACE:
Whom God hath joined, Epworth Press, London

WINIFRED BROWN:
The Partnership of Christian Marriage, East Africa Literature Bureau, Nairobi

Handbook of Preparation for Christian Marriage, Christian Council of Ghana

Twenty Awkward Questions and Twenty Frank Answers, Daystar Press, Ibadan

C. K. DOVLO:
Christianity and Family Life in Ghana, Presbyterian Book Depot, Accra

DOUGLAS S. HUBERY:
Why Shouldn't We? Chester House Publications, London

WALTER TROBISCH:
I Loved a Girl . . ., U. S. C. L., London